70s Guitar Clas

AUTHENTIC TRANSCRIPTIONS
WITH NOTES AND TABLATURE

HLE

HAL LEONARD EUROPE

Distributed by Music Sales

Exclusive Distributors:
Music Sales Limited
8/9 Frith Street, London W1V 5TZ, England.
Music Sales Pty Limited
120 Rothschild Avenue, Rosebery, NSW 2018, Australia.

Order No. HLE90000605
ISBN 0-7119-7972-3

Cover design by Mike Bell Design.
Photography by George Taylor.
Guitar kindly loaned by Rhodes World of Music.
Printed in the USA.

Your Guarantee of Quality:
As publishers, we strive to produce every book to the highest commercial standards.
The book has been carefully designed to minimise awkward page turns and
to make playing from it a real pleasure.
Throughout, the printing and binding have been planned to ensure a
sturdy, attractive publication which should give years of enjoyment.
If your copy fails to meet our high standards, please inform us and we will gladly replace it.

Music Sales' complete catalogue describes thousands of
titles and is available in full colour sections by subject, direct from Music Sales Limited.
Please state your areas of interest and send a cheque/postal order for £1.50 for postage to:
Music Sales Limited, Newmarket Road, Bury St. Edmunds, Suffolk IP33 3YB, England.

www.musicsales.com

Guitar Notation Legend

Guitar Music can be notated three different ways: on a *musical staff*, in *tablature*, and in *rhythm slashes*.

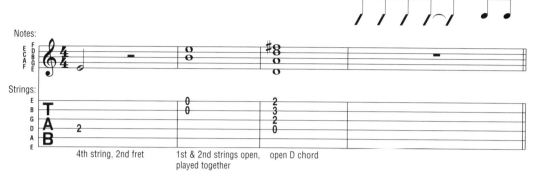

RHYTHM SLASHES are written above the staff. Strum chords in the rhythm indicated. Use the chord diagrams found at the top of the first page of the transcription for the appropriate chord voicings. Round noteheads indicate single notes.

THE MUSICAL STAFF shows pitches and rhythms and is divided by bar lines into measures. Pitches are named after the first seven letters of the alphabet.

TABLATURE graphically represents the guitar fingerboard. Each horizontal line represents a string, and each number represents a fret.

4th string, 2nd fret — 1st & 2nd strings open, played together — open D chord

---

HALF-STEP BEND: Strike the note and bend up 1/2 step.

WHOLE-STEP BEND: Strike the note and bend up one step.

GRACE NOTE BEND: Strike the note and bend up as indicated. The first note does not take up any time.

SLIGHT (MICROTONE) BEND: Strike the note and bend up 1/4 step.

BEND AND RELEASE: Strike the note and bend up as indicated, then release back to the original note. Only the first note is struck.

PRE-BEND: Bend the note as indicated, then strike it.

VIBRATO: The string is vibrated by rapidly bending and releasing the note with the fretting hand.

WIDE VIBRATO: The pitch is varied to a greater degree by vibrating with the fretting hand.

HAMMER-ON: Strike the first (lower) note with one finger, then sound the higher note (on the same string) with another finger by fretting it without picking.

PULL-OFF: Place both fingers on the notes to be sounded. Strike the first note and without picking, pull the finger off to sound the second (lower) note.

LEGATO SLIDE: Strike the first note and then slide the same fret-hand finger up or down to the second note. The second note is not struck.

SHIFT SLIDE: Same as legato slide, except the second note is struck.

TRILL: Very rapidly alternate between the notes indicated by continuously hammering on and pulling off.

TAPPING: Hammer ("tap") the fret indicated with the pick-hand index or middle finger and pull off to the note fretted by the fret hand.

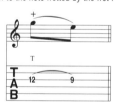

NATURAL HARMONIC: Strike the note while the fret-hand lightly touches the string directly over the fret indicated.

PINCH HARMONIC: The note is fretted normally and a harmonic is produced by adding the edge of the thumb or the tip of the index finger of the pick hand to the normal pick attack.

PICK SCRAPE: The edge of the pick is rubbed down (or up) the string, producing a scratchy sound.

MUFFLED STRINGS: A percussive sound is produced by laying the fret hand across the string(s) without depressing, and striking them with the pick hand.

PALM MUTING: The note is partially muted by the pick hand lightly touching the string(s) just before the bridge.

RAKE: Drag the pick across the strings indicated with a single motion.

TREMOLO PICKING: The note is picked as rapidly and continuously as possible.

VIBRATO BAR DIVE AND RETURN: The pitch of the note or chord is dropped a specified number of steps (in rhythm) then returned to the original pitch.

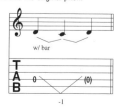

VIBRATO BAR SCOOP: Depress the bar just before striking the note, then quickly release the bar.

VIBRATO BAR DIP: Strike the note and then immediately drop a specified number of steps, then release back to the original pitch.

All Right Now

Words and Music by Paul Rodgers and Andy Fraser

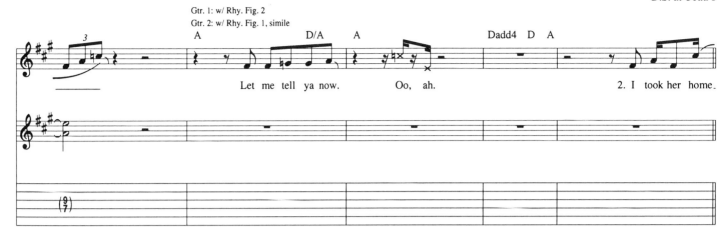

Coda 1

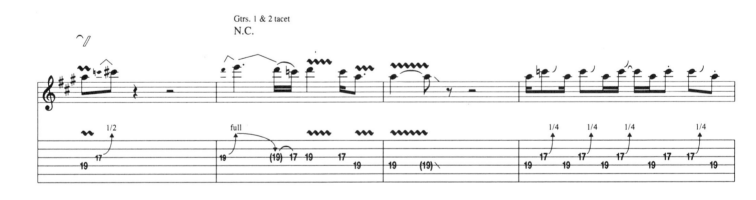

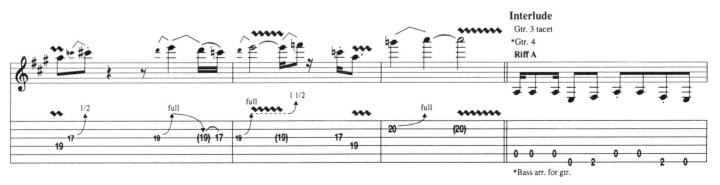

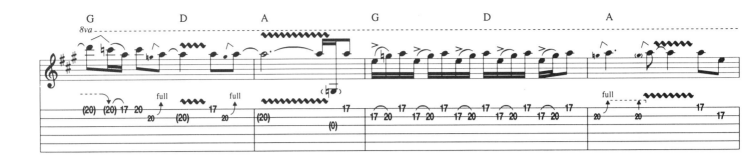

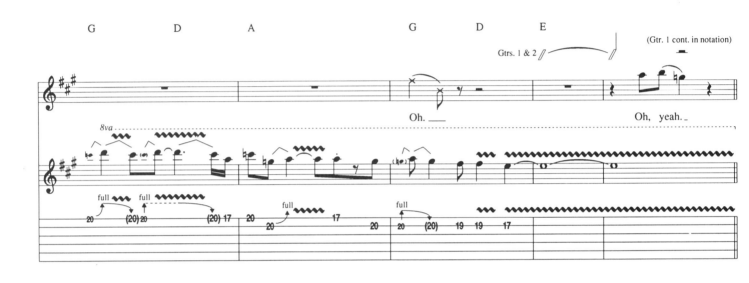

Bridge

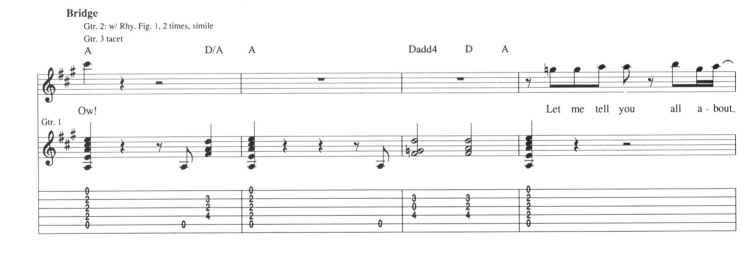

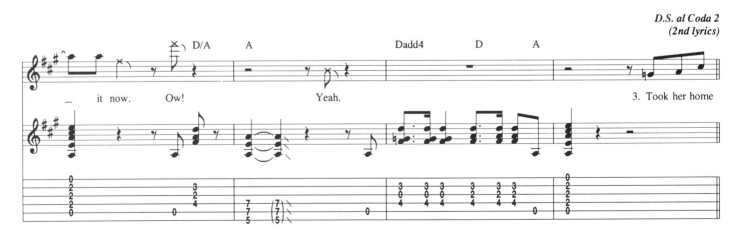

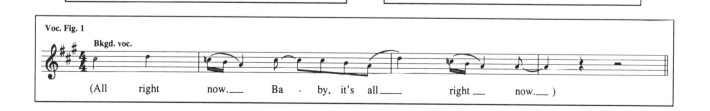

The Boys Are Back In Town

Words and Music by Philip Parris Lynott

*1st time only

1. Guess who just got back __ to - day. __ Them wild - eyed _ boys _ that had been a - way. _
2. You know that chick that used to dance a lot? Every night she'd be on the floor shakin' what she got. _
3. Fri - day night they'll be dressed to kill down at Dino's Bar and Grill.

Haven't changed, hadn't much to say,
Man, when I tell you she was cool, she was red hot!
The drink will flow and blood will spill, and if the

but man, I still think them cats are crazy.
I mean she was steamin'!
boys wanna fight you better let'em.

They were askin' if you were around,
And that time over at Johnny's place,
That juke-box in the corner blastin' out my favorite song.

how you was, where you could be found.
well this chick got up and she slapped Johnny's face.
The nights are getting warm and it won't be long.

11

boys ___ are back in town. ___ The boys ___ are back in town. ___ The boys ___ are back in town. ___

The boys

___ are back in town. ___

Bridge

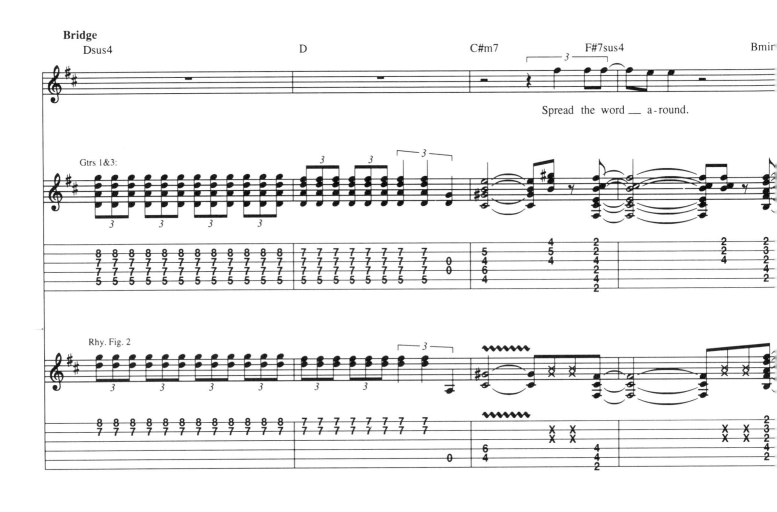

Spread the word __ a-round.

Guess who's back in town. __

You __ spread the word a-round.

⊕ *Coda*

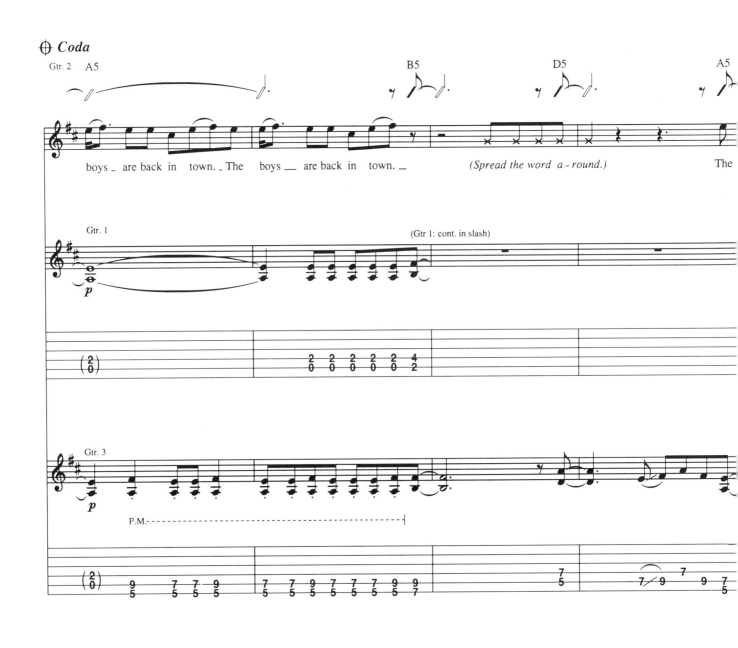

boys __ are back in town. __ The boys __ are back in town. __   *(Spread the word a-round.)*   The

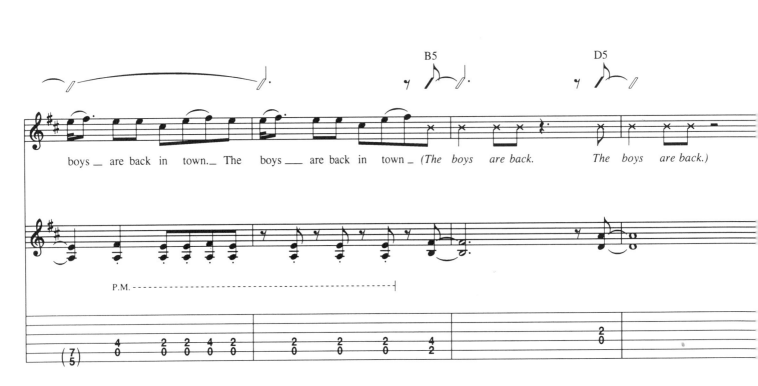

boys __ are back in town. __ The boys __ are back in town __ *(The boys are back.   The boys are back.)*

The boys __ are back __ in town __ a - gain. __

'Been hang - in' down __ at Di - no's __

The boys are back in town a - gain.

Detroit Rock City

Words and Music by Paul Stanley and Bob Ezrin

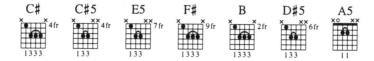

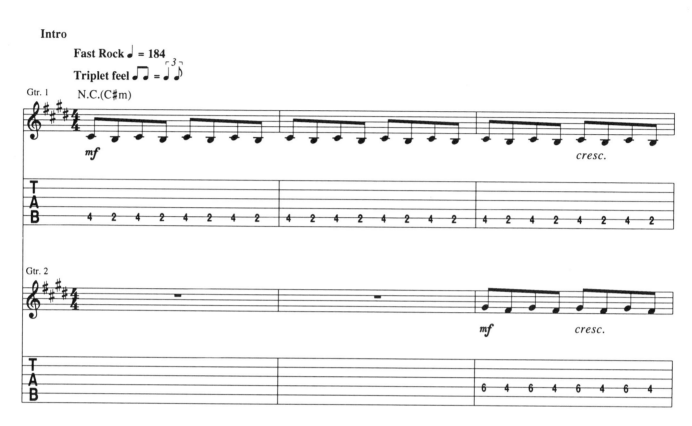

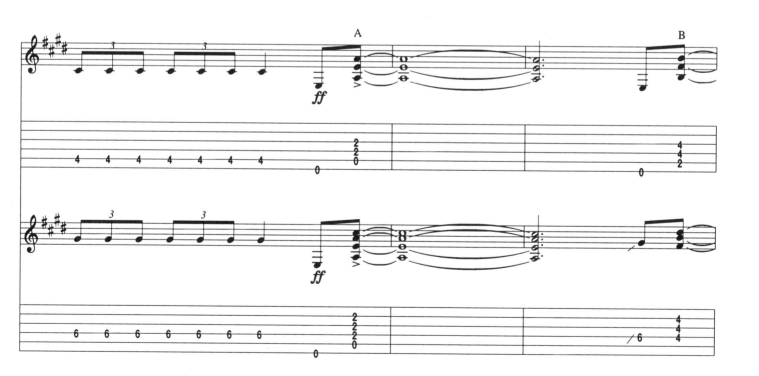

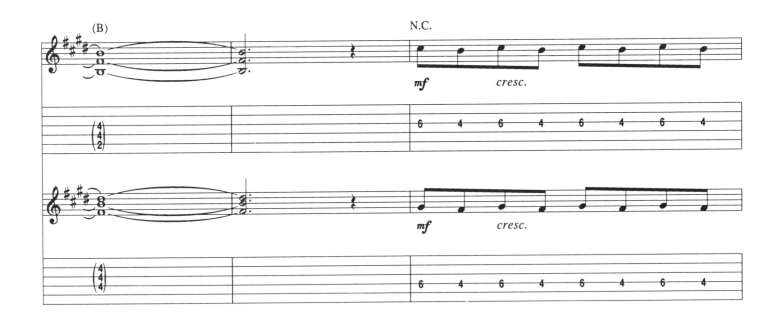

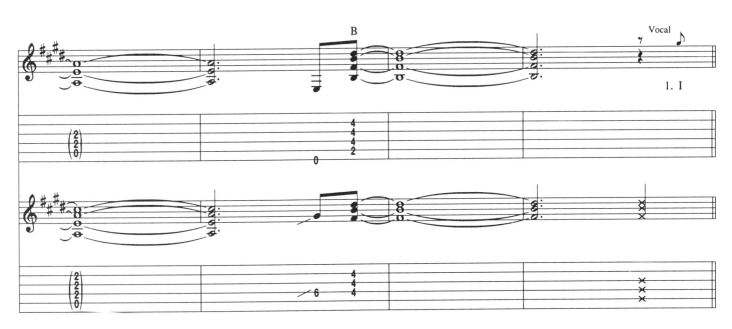

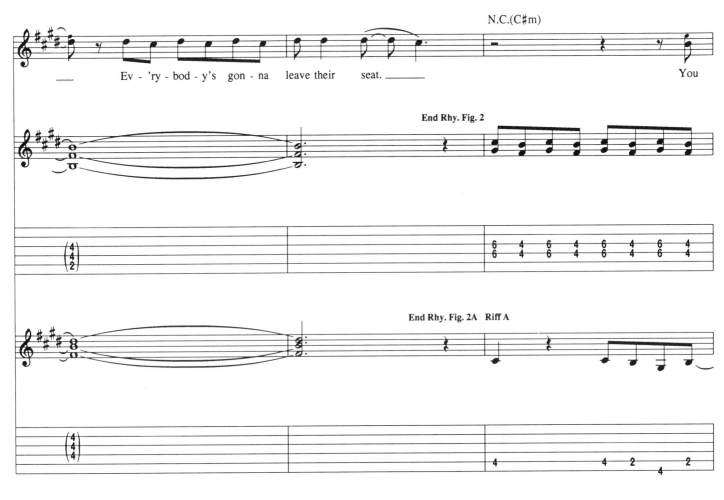

N.C.(C#m)

Ev - 'ry - bod - y's gon - na leave their seat. ____ You

End Rhy. Fig. 2

End Rhy. Fig. 2A Riff A

got - ta lose your mind in De - troit Rock Cit - y. Get up! ___

End Riff A

Verse

Gtrs. 1 & 2: w/Rhy. Fig. 1

2. Get-tin' late, _ I just can't wait. Ten o' - clock, _ and I

know I got-ta hit the road. _____ First I drink, then I smoke.

Start up the car, _ and I try to make the mid-night show. _____ Get up!_

Chorus

Gtr. 1: w/Rhy. Fig. 2
Gtr. 2: w/Rhy. Fig. 2A

_ Ev-'ry-bod-y's gon-na move their feet. Get down!_ Ev-'ry-bod-y's gon-na leave their seat. _____

feel so good; I'm so a-live. __   Hear my song __

Chorus

play-in' on the ra-di-o. _____   It goes: __   Get up! __ Ev-'ry-bod-y's gon-na

move their feet.   Get down! __ Ev-'ry-bod-y's gon-na leave their seat. _____

Interlude

move their feet._____ (Get down!) __

Get up! _____ Ev - 'ry - bod - y's gon - na

leave their seat, _____ get down! __

Fill 1
Gtrs. 1 & 2

Iron Man

Words and Music by Frank Iommi, John Osbourne, William Ward and Terence Butler

Intro
Slow Rock ♩ = 69

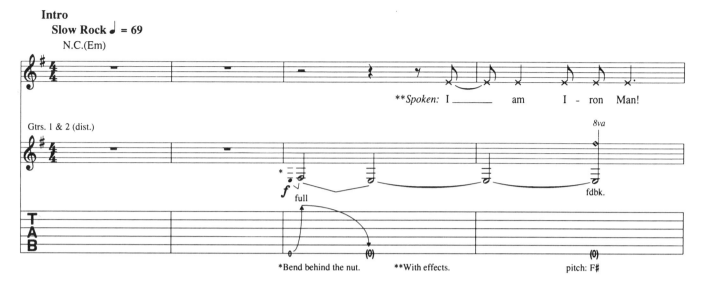

*Bend behind the nut. **With effects. pitch: F#

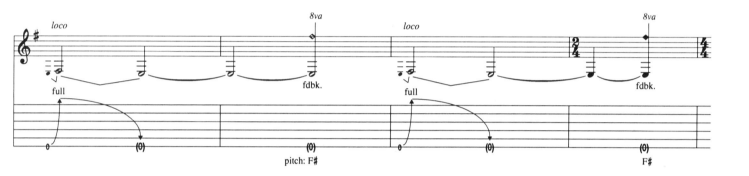

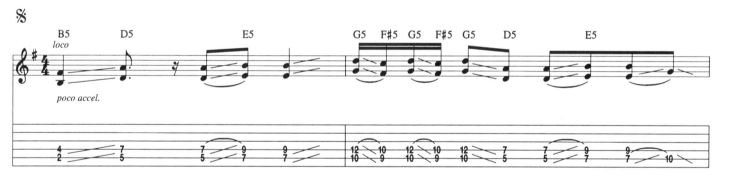

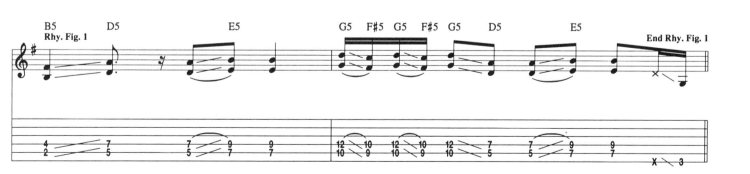

Verse

Gtrs. 1 & 2: w/ Riff A, 2 times

3. He was turned to steel in ___ the ___ great ___ mag - net - ic field,
4. Now the time is here for ___ I - ron Man ___ to spread fear.

when he trav - elled time for ___ the - fu - ture of man - kind.
Venge - ance from the grave, kills ___ the ___ peo - ple he once saved.

Bridge

No-bod-y wants ___ him, ___ he just stares ___ at the world. ___
No-bod-y wants ___ him, ___ they just turn ___ their ___ heads. ___

Gtrs. 1 & 2
Rhy. Fig. 2   End Rhy. Fig. 2   Riff B   End Riff B

Gtrs. 1 & 2: w/ Rhy. Fig. 2   Gtrs. 1 & 2: w/ Riff B

Plan-ning his venge-ance ___ that he will ___ soon un - furl. ___
No - bod - y helps ___ him, ___ now he has ___ his re - venge. ___

Interlude

Double - Time ♩ = 164

N.C.(C♯m)

Gtrs. 1 & 2 **Riff C**   **End Riff C**

Guitar Solo

Gtr. 2 tacet

Gtr. 1   N.C.(C#m)

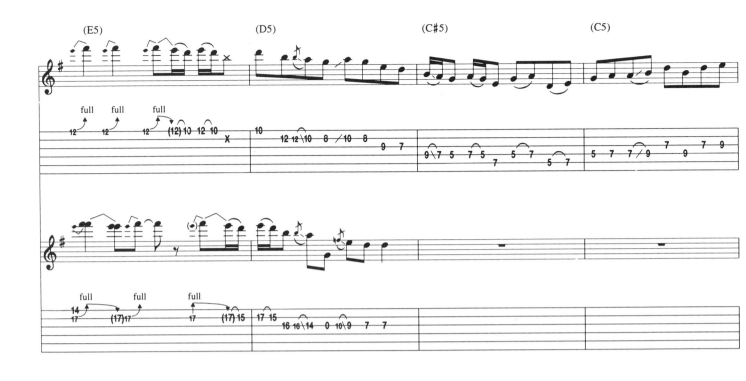

Outro

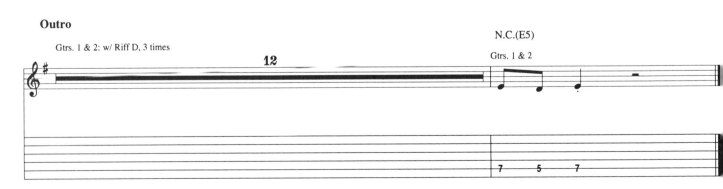

Message in a Bottle

Words and Music by Sting

Pre-Chorus

I'll send __ an S. __ O. __ S. __ to the world. I'll send __ an S. __ O. __ S. __ to the world.

I hope __ that some - one gets __ my, I hope __ that some - one gets __ my,

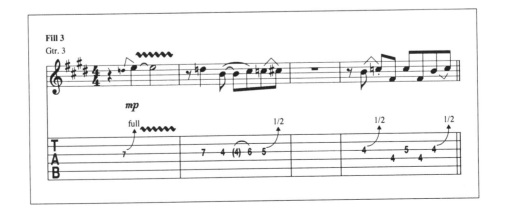

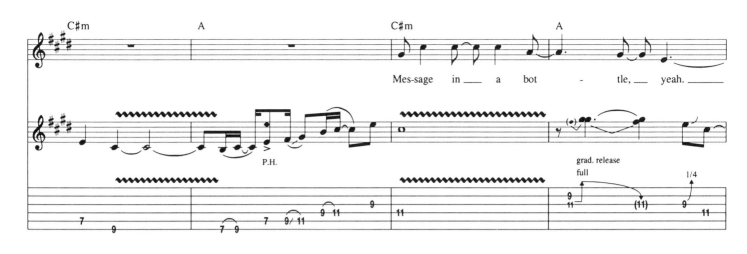

Mes-sage in a bot-tle, yeah.

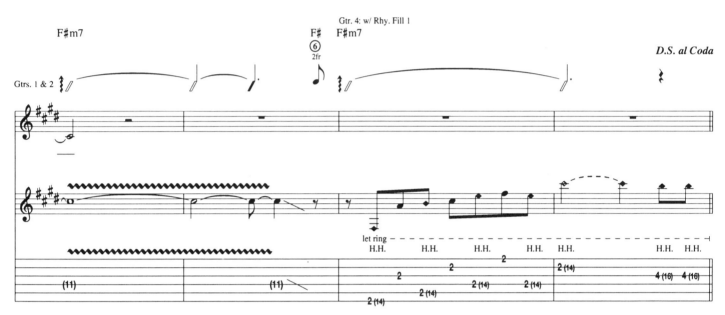

D.S. al Coda

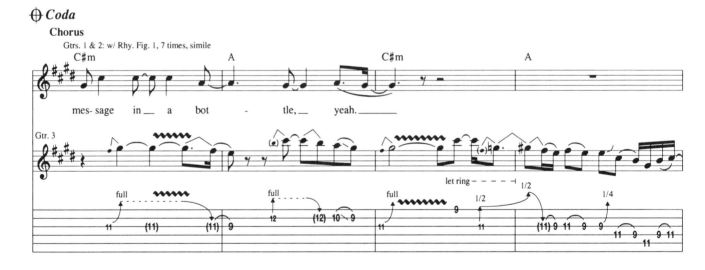

mes-sage in a bot-tle, yeah.

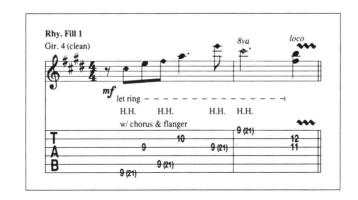

Additional Lyrics

Woke up this morning,
I don't believe what I saw.
Hundred billion bottles washed up on the shore.
Seems I never noticed being alone.
Hundred billion castaways,
Looking for a home.

40

More Than a Feeling

Words and Music by Tom Scholz

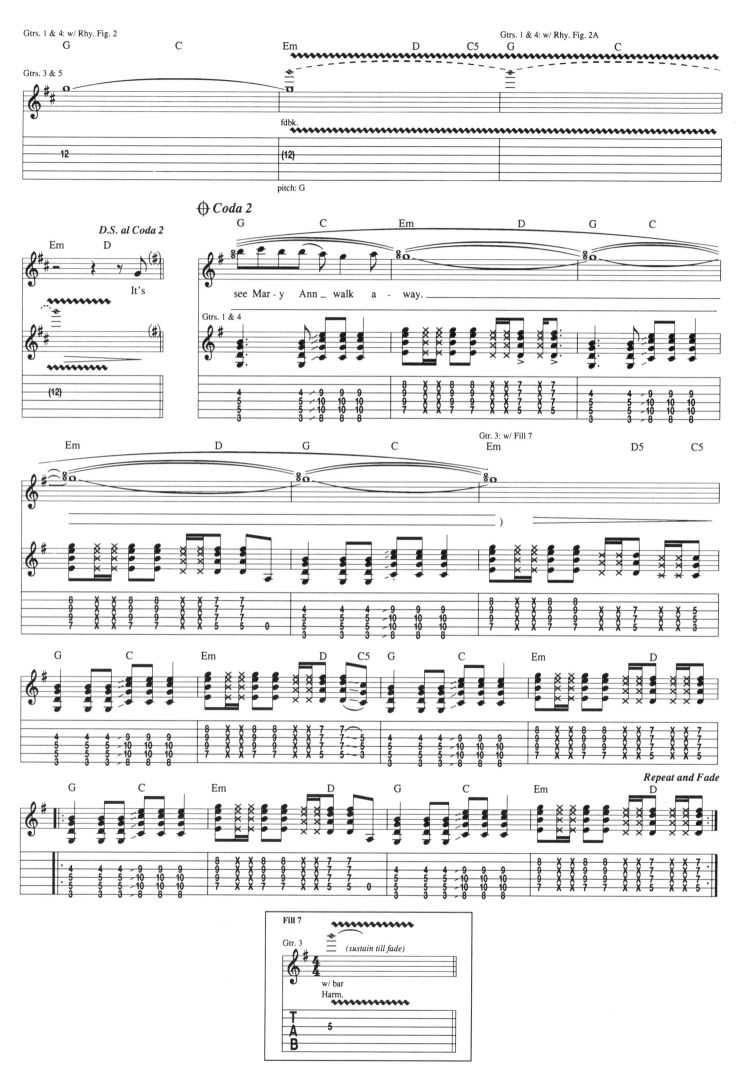

Reelin' in the Years

Words and Music by Walter Becker and Donald Fagen

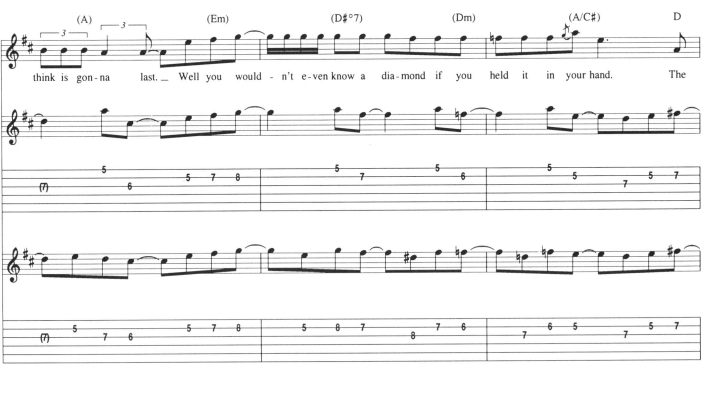

think is gon-na last. __ Well you would-n't e-ven know a dia-mond if you held it in your hand. The

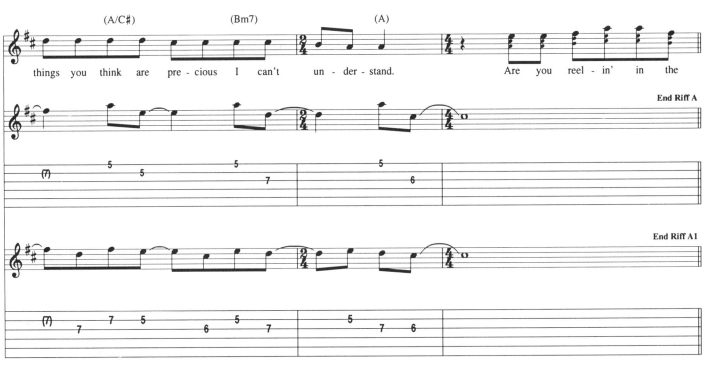

things you think are pre-cious I can't un-der-stand. Are you reel-in' in the

End Riff A

End Riff A1

Chorus

Gtr. 3 tacet

years; __ stow-in' a-way the time? __ Are you gath-er-in' up the

Gtr. 2 Rhy. Fig. 1

years; — stow-in' a-way the time? — Are you gath-er-in' up the

tears? — Have you had e-nough of mine? —

Interlude

Fill 1
Gtr. 2

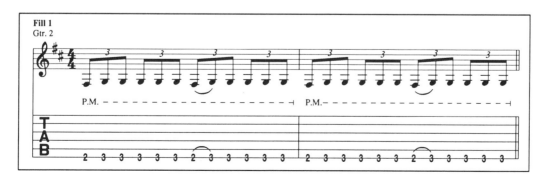

56

Are you gath-er-in' up the tears? _____ Have you had e-nough of

mine? _____

Interlude

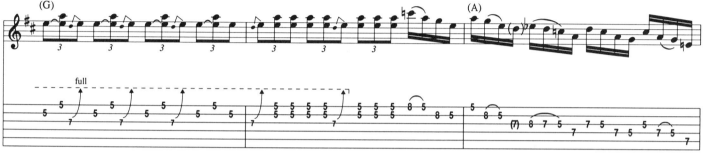

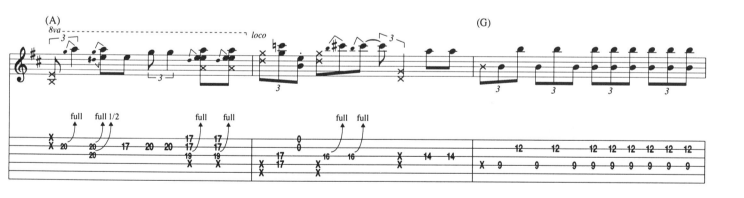

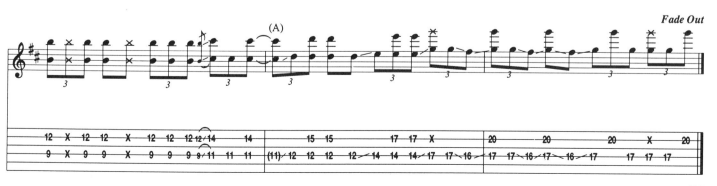

Rocky Mountain Way

Words and Music by Joe Walsh, Joe Vitale, Ken Passarelli and Rocke Grace

* Key signature denotes E Mixolydian.

* Composite arr.

*Played between the 11th and 12th frets.

MCA Music Publishing

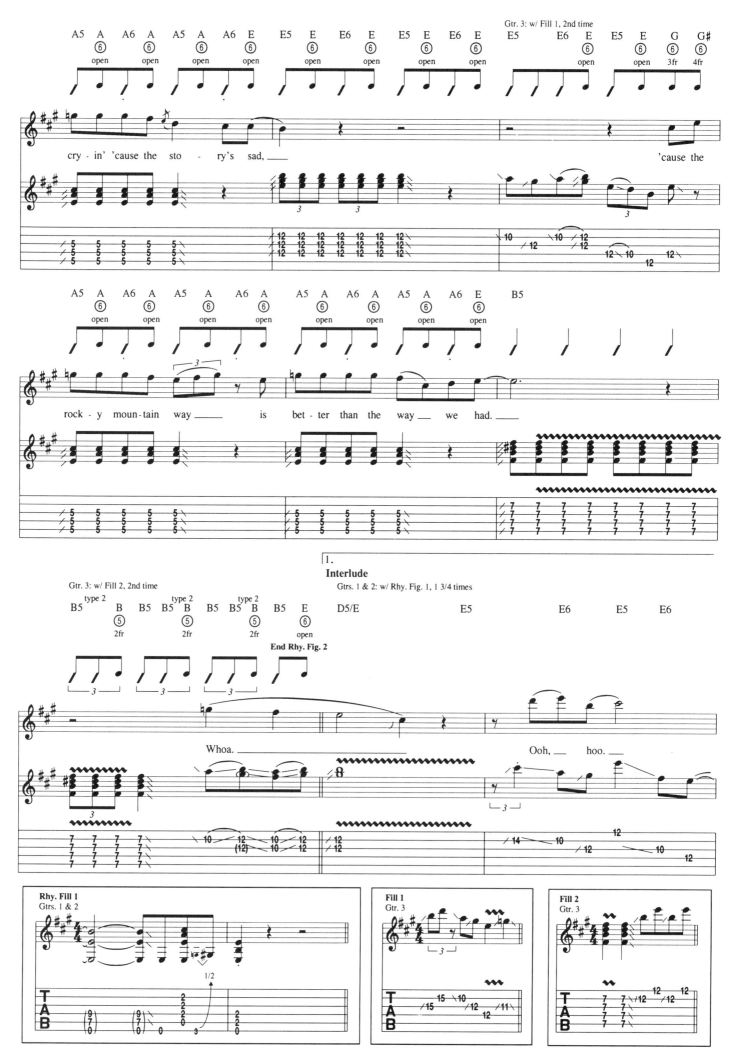

2. Well, he's

*Chord Symbols implied by kybd.

Sweet Home Alabama

Words and Music by Ronnie Van Zant, Ed King and Gary Rossington

bam - a,   Lord, I'm com-in' home to you.

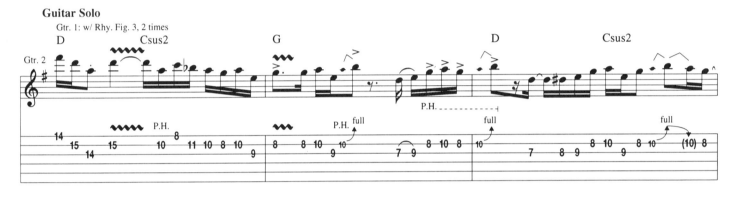

Guitar Solo

Verse

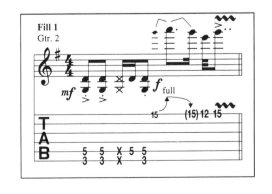

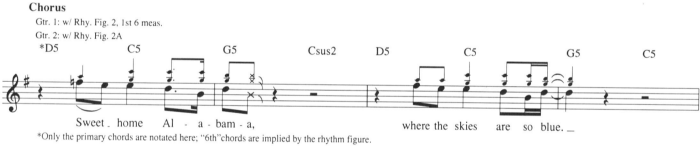

Chorus

*Only the primary chords are notated here; "6th" chords are implied by the rhythm figure.

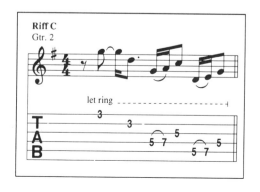

Guitar Solo

Gtr. 1: w/ Rhy. Fig. 4

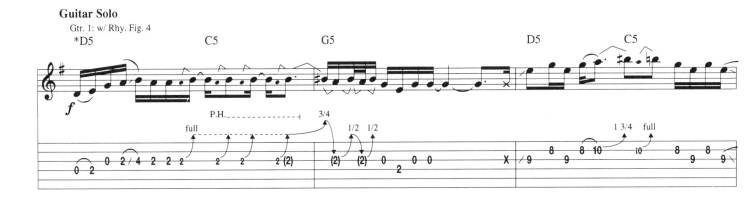

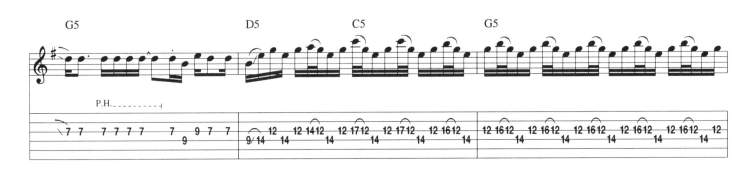

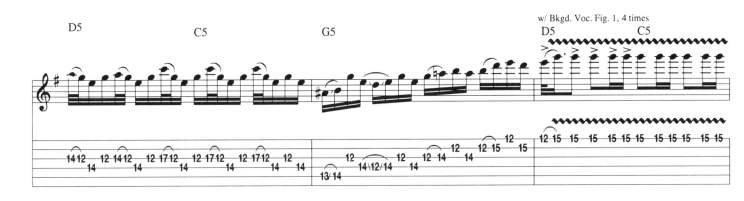

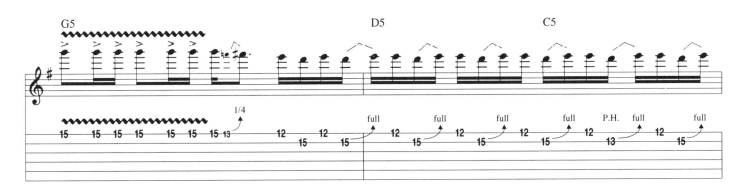

Fill 2
Gtr. 2

Bkgd. Voc. Fig. 1

Ah,   ah,   ah,   Al-a-bam-a!

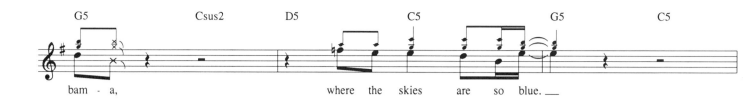

bam - a,   where the skies   are   so blue. __

Sweet __ home Al - a - bam - a,   Lord, I'm com - in' home to you!

Gtr. 1: w/ Rhy. Fig. 2
Gtr. 2: w/ Rhy. Fig. 2A

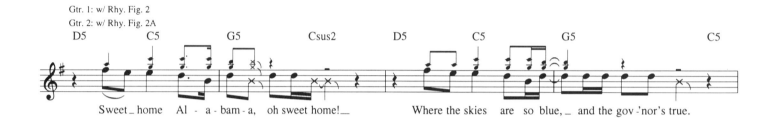

Sweet __ home Al - a - bam - a, oh sweet home! __   Where the skies   are so blue, __ and the gov-'nor's true.

Gtrs. 1 & 2: w/ Rhy. Fig. 4

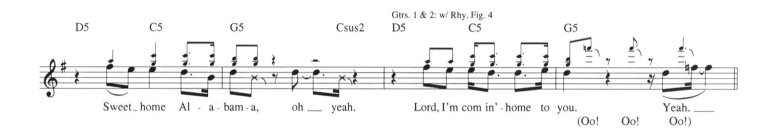

Sweet __ home Al - a - bam - a,   oh __ yeah.   Lord, I'm com in' - home to you.   Yeah. __
                                                                                                  (Oo!   Oo!   Oo!)

Play 6 times and Fade

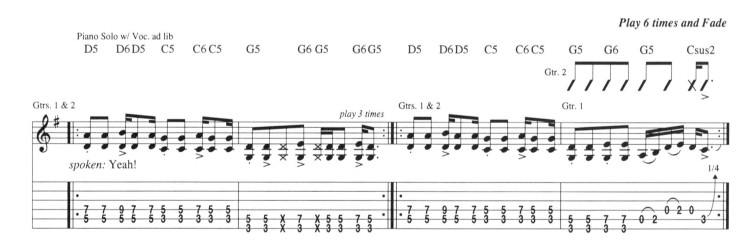

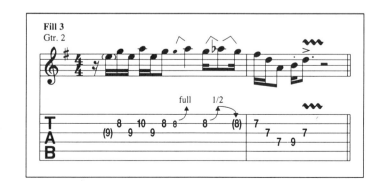

74

Takin' Care of Business

Words and Music by Randy Bachman

They

Verse

Rhy. Fig. 1

Gtrs. 1 & 2

1., 3. get up ev - 'ry morn - ing from the a - larm clock's warn - ing. Take the eight fif - teen in - to the
2. eas - y as fish - ing you could be a mu - si - cian, if you could make sounds loud and

End Rhy. Fig. 1

Gtrs. 1 & 2: w/ Rhy. Fig. 1, 3 times, simile

cit - y. There's a whis - tle up a - bove and peo - ple push - ing, peo - ple shov - ing, and the
mel - low. Get a sec - ond hand gui - tar, chanc - es are you'll go far if

Gtr. 2: w/ Fill 2, 3rd time

girls who try to look pret - ty. And if your train's on time you can
get in with the right bunch of fel - lows. Peo - ple see you hav - ing fun just a -

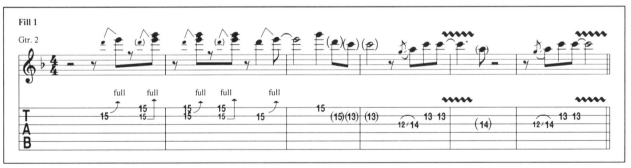

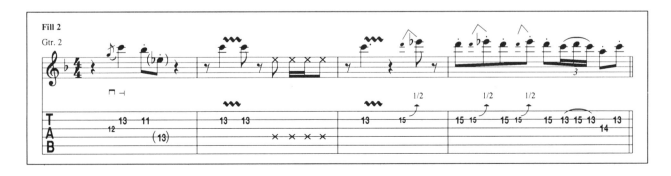

Guitar Solo
Gtr. 3 tacet

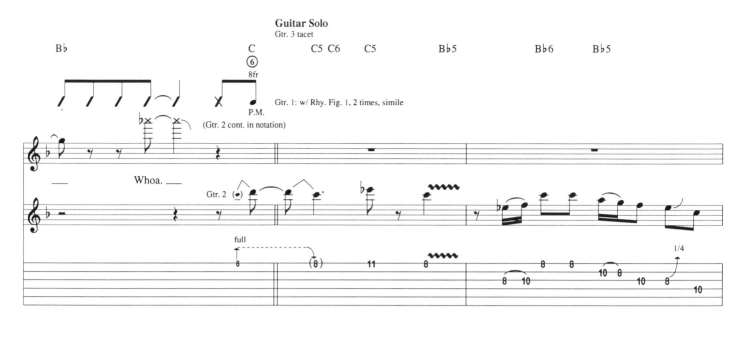

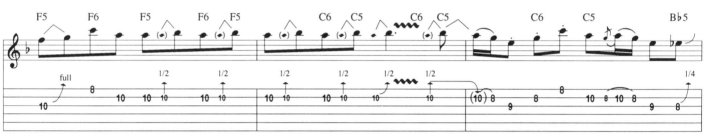

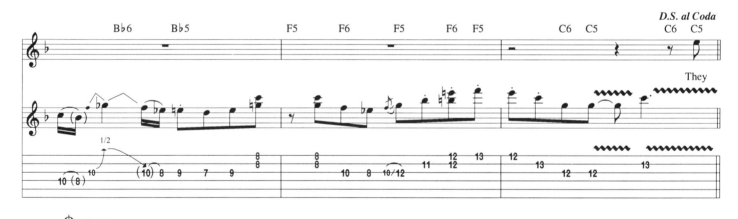

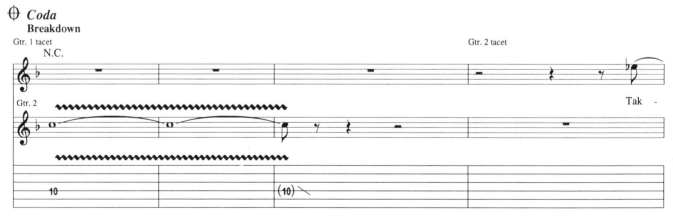

⊕ *Coda*
Breakdown

80

Walk This Way

Words and Music by Steven Tyler and Joe Perry

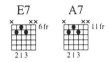

ain't seen noth-in' till you're down on a muf-fin and you're sure to be a-chang-in' your ways." I met a
three young la-dies in the school gym lock-er when I no-ticed they was look-in' at me. I was a

P.M.

Gtr. 3: w/ Rhy. Fill 2, 2nd time

cheer - lead - er, was a real young bleed-er all the times I could rem - i - nisce, 'cause the
high school los - er, nev-er made it with a la-dy 'til the boys told me some-thin' I missed, then my

Rhy. Fig. 2

P.M.

A5

best things in lov-in' with a sis-ter and a cou-sin on - ly start-ed with a lit-tle kiss, a - like this!
next door neigh-bor with a daugh-ter had a fav - or so I gave her just a lit-tle kiss a - like this!

End Rhy. Fig. 2

P.M.

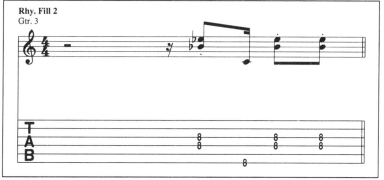

Rhy. Fill 2
Gtr. 3

Interlude

Gtr. 1: w/ Riff A, 2nd time

N.C.(E5)

Verse

Gtrs. 1 & 2: w/ Rhy. Fig. 1, 3 times, simile

N.C.(C7)

2., 4. See - saw swing-in' with the boys in the school and your feet fly-in' up in the air, ___ I sing,

"Hey did - dle did - dle" with your kit - ty in the mid - dle of the swing like you did - n't care. ___ So I

took a big chance at the high school dance with a miss - y who was read - y to play, ___ was a

* Sing harmony 1st time only.

86

Guitar Solo

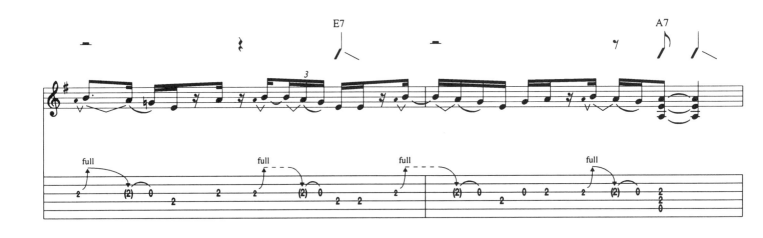

Begin Fade

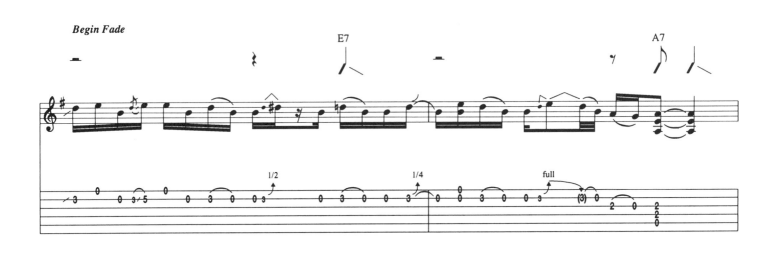

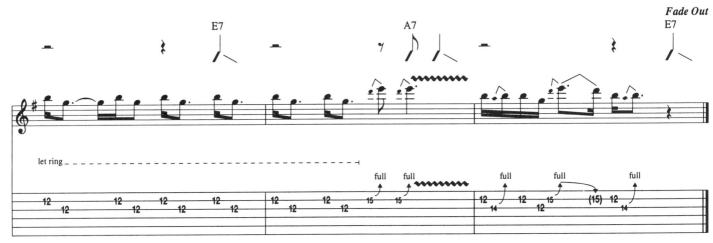

You Really Got Me

Words and Music by Ray Davies

*Flick toggle switch between on & off pickup
selection to create specified rhythm. Rhythm shown
is only for the "on" position sound.

Interlude

Gtr. 1 tacet
N.C.

Ah. ___ Ah. ___ Ah. ___ Ah. ___ Ah. ___
(Ah, ah, ah, ah. Ah, ah. Chu, chu, chu, chu, chu, ch, ch.)

Verse

w/ ad lib vocal effects
N.C.

3. Girl, you real-ly got me now, you got me so I don't know what I'm do-in'. ___

Ah. Girl, you real-ly got me now, you got me so I can't sleep at night! ___

Girl, you real-ly got me now, you got me so I don't know where I'm go-in', ___
(Girl, ___